# HERGÉ
★
## THE ADVENTURES OF
# TINTIN
★
# THE
# BROKEN
# EAR

EGMONT

**The TINTIN books are published in the following languages:**

| | |
|---|---|
| Alsacien | CASTERMAN |
| Basque | ELKAR |
| Bengali | ANANDA |
| Bernese | EMMENTALER DRUCK |
| Breton | AN HERE |
| Catalan | CASTERMAN |
| Chinese | CASTERMAN/CHINA CHILDREN PUBLISHING |
| Corsican | CASTERMAN |
| Danish | CARLSEN |
| Dutch | CASTERMAN |
| English | EGMONT UK LTD/LITTLE, BROWN & CO. |
| Esperanto | ESPERANTIX/CASTERMAN |
| Finnish | OTAVA |
| French | CASTERMAN |
| Gallo | RUE DES SCRIBES |
| Gaumais | CASTERMAN |
| German | CARLSEN |
| Greek | CASTERMAN |
| Hebrew | MIZRAHI |
| Indonesian | INDIRA |
| Italian | CASTERMAN |
| Japanese | FUKUINKAN |
| Korean | CASTERMAN/SOL |
| Latin | ELI/CASTERMAN |
| Luxembourgeois | IMPRIMERIE SAINT-PAUL |
| Norwegian | EGMONT |
| Picard | CASTERMAN |
| Polish | CASTERMAN/MOTOPOL |
| Portuguese | CASTERMAN |
| Provençal | CASTERMAN |
| Romanche | LIGIA ROMONTSCHA |
| Russian | CASTERMAN |
| Serbo-Croatian | DECJE NOVINE |
| Spanish | CASTERMAN |
| Swedish | CARLSEN |
| Thai | CASTERMAN |
| Tibetan | CASTERMAN |
| Turkish | YAPI KREDI YAYINLARI |

TRANSLATED BY
LESLIE LONSDALE-COOPER AND MICHAEL TURNER

# EGMONT
*We bring stories to life*

Artwork copyright © 1945 by Editions Casterman, Paris and Tournai
Copyright © renewed 1984 by Casterman
Text copyright © 1975 by Egmont UK Limited
First published in Great Britain in 1975 by Methuen Children's Books
Hardback edition published in 2003, paperback edition published in 2010 by
Egmont UK Limited, The Yellow Building, 1 Nicholas Road, London, W11 4AN

Library of Congress Catalogue Card Numbers Afor 825 and TX 475050

Hardback: ISBN 978 1 4052 0805 5
Paperback: ISBN 978 1 4052 0617 4

PAINTED POSTS DAHOMEY

BAPENDE MASK

HEAD OF CARVED WOOD PACHACAMAO

No. 3542
ARUMBAYA FETISH
The Arumbaya tribe live along the banks of the River Coliflor in the Republic of San Theodoros, South America

Closing time!

Goodness! It's five o'clock already . . .

RRRRING

Come on, lazy-bones! Time to get up!

Toreador, on guard now!
Toreador! Toreador!
Toreador!

Toreador . . . tra la la la la . . . Toreador . . . Fond eyes gaze and adore . . .

PLURIARC BURMA

Knees bent, arms full stretch! Ready . . . up . . . and down . . . and up . . . and down . . .

Now for a bath; that's the way to wake up in the morning.

Here is the eight o'clock news . . .

Details are just coming in of a robbery at the Museum of Ethnography. A rare fetish - a sacred tribal object - disappeared during the night . . .

The loss was discovered this morning by a museum attendant. It is believed the thief must have hidden in the gallery overnight and slipped out when the staff arrived for work. No evidence of a break-in has been found . . .

Come on Snowy! To the Museum of Ethnography!

The Director? I'm afraid he's engaged: the police are here . . .

Now, to recapitulate . . . You say the attendant locked the doors last night at 17.12 hours; he noticed nothing unusual. He came on duty this morning at seven. At 07.14 he observed that exhibit No. 3542 was missing and immediately raised the alarm. Right? . . . Now this attendant: is he reliable?

Absolutely! Above suspicion! He's been with us for over twelve years and never given the least cause for complaint.

Besides, the fetish has no intrinsic value. In my judgement, it would only be of interest to a collector . . .

Great snakes! The Thompsons!

Why, it's our friend Tintin!

Have you any leads?

Well, the Arumbaya fetish has no in . . . er . . . no instinctive value . . . The solution is quite simple: it was removed by a collector.

To be precise: it was collect-ed by a remover.

Some hours later . . .

This is the book. I'm sure it has something about the Arumbayas.

A.J. WALKER

TRAVELS IN THE AMERICAS

LONDON 1875

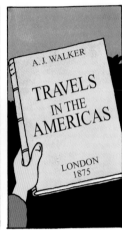

Aha! This is interesting . . . Listen, Snowy. "Today we met our first Arumbayas. Long, black, oily hair framed their coffee-coloured faces. They were armed with long blow-pipes which they employ to shoot darts poisoned with curare . . ." You hear that, Snowy?

We decided to stay there. The sur generosity and gave us a plentiful

fig 123
ARUMBAYA
armed with a blow-pipe

. . . Curare! . . . the terrible vegetable poison which paralyses one's breathing! . . . Oh! "Arumbaya fetish" . . . But . . . but . . . it's the very one that's been stolen!

I therefore made an accurate sketch they urged me to g

fig 123
ARUMBAYA FETISH
we were very well treated. Later we

Odd coincidence, don't you think, Snowy? . . . Snowy isn't interested . . . he's gone to sleep . . . I think I'll follow suit.

The next morning . . .

Help! It's bewitched!

Hello! . . . Hello? . . . Hello!? . . . Is that you, sir?

Yes, who is that? . . . Oh, it's you, Fred . . . What? The fetish? . . . My goodness me! I'll come at once . . .

Extraordinary! There was the fetish this morning, back in its usual place, with this letter propped up beside it . . . What do you think?

Hmmm!

Hmm?

In my opinion, gentlemen, the fetish is bewitched!

Dear Director,
I bet a friend I could pinch something from your museum.
I won my bet, so here's your fetish back.
Please forgive my foolishness, and any trouble I have caused.
Sincerely,
X

No. 3542
ARUMBAYA FETISH
The Arumbaya tribe live along the banks of the River Coliflor in the Republic of San Theodoros,

My mind is made up: this letter is anonymous. Nobody knows who wrote it!

To be precise: I agree. An anonymous letter nobody wrote!

According to the police the case is closed . . . But that isn't my view . . .

Why doesn't he give up?

I do beg your pardon, sir!

Wake up, Tintin! Look where you're going!

So, am I the only one to know the fetish they put back is a fake?

Here's the proof. Walker, the explorer, says he made an "accurate sketch". And according to the drawing . . .

. . . the right ear of the fetish is slightly damaged: there's a little bit missing.

ARUMBAYA FETISH

But on the reinstated fetish the right ear is intact. So it must be a copy . . . Now, who would be interested in acquiring the real one? A collector? Quite possibly . . . Anyway, let's see what the press has to say about it.

Oh dear, here we go again . . . Sherlock Holmes on the trail!

### FATAL OVERSIGHT

A strong smell of gas alerted residents this morning at 21 London Road. They sent for the police who effected an entry to the room occupied by artist Jacob Balthazar. Officers discovered the sculptor lying on his bed; he was found to be dead. It appears that the victim had forgotten to turn off the tap on his gas-ring. By some chance his parrot survived the fumes.

Mr. Balthazar's work attracted the attention of art-critics, who particularly praised his series of wooden statuettes, his special technique being strongly reminiscent of primitive sculpture.

◆

Going round and round like that, he makes me giddy!

Half an hour later . . .

Excuse me . . . Is this the house where Mr Balthazar lived?

Yes, this is it. Ooh, sir, what a tragedy! . . . Such a polite gentleman! . . . And all that learning! . . . Maybe he wasn't all that regular with the rent, but he always paid it in the end. And such a way with animals! A parrot and three white mice, that's what he had . . .

I . . .

I'm minding the parrot for the time being. But I can't keep it. So if you know of anyone . . .

Of course . . . I was wondering if I might look at Mr Balthazar's room?

I'll take you up. Such a character he was . . . sniff . . . I can still see him . . . his everlasting black velvet suit, and that big hat . . . And all that smoking! A pipe in his mouth all day long, he had. But he never touched the drink . . .

Oh?

Here is his room . . .

This is where we found him . . . sniff . . . They had to send for a locksmith . . . the door was locked from the inside . . . The gas was whistling out of the ring.

A little scrap of grey flannel . . .

And so clever he was . . . Just look at those flowers: you can almost smell them . . .

You knew Mr Balthazar well?

Er . . . that's to say . . . not intimately . . .

If by any chance you found a parrot-lover . . . It's such a friendly bird!

Naturally, I'll remember you. Goodbye and thanks.

An accident? . . . Funny sort of accident, I'd say . . .

A very funny accident! . . . The gas was whistling out of the ring. So, if the tap was on when Balthazar went to bed he'd have heard it. Unless he was drunk; but he never touched drink. Therefore someone turned the tap on after the sculptor was dead, since the gas wasn't strong enough to kill the parrot. And that someone was wearing something made of grey flannel and smoking a cigarette . . .

. . . witness the piece of cloth and the cigarette end, which couldn't have belonged to the victim: he only smoked a pipe, and he wore a velvet suit. So Mr Balthazar was murdered. He was murdered because he'd probably made a replica of the Arumbaya fetish for someone. And someone didn't want him to talk . . . Someone? . . . Someone? . . . Who can that 'someone' be? . . . How can I find out?

Great snakes! . . . Why not?!

Excuse me, but I've been thinking. I'll buy Mr Balthazar's parrot.

The parrot? Ooooh, sir!

If you'd only been two minutes sooner! I just sold it. The gentleman who bought it was here a moment ago; you must have passed him.

Just my luck!

Look, there he goes! You see the gentleman with a parcel under his arm? That's him.

Let's hope he'll agree to resell it to me.

Grrreat greedy-guts!

Hey, you! . . . D'you always behave like that? Let me tell you, I'm not used to being insulted!

Perdone, Señor.

Very well! But another time you'll be in trouble!

But . . . I assure the señor . . .

GRRREAT GREEDY-GUTS!

Oh, help! It's a regular punch-up . . . Ooh! The parrot! The parrot!!

The parrot!!!

GRRREAT GREEDY-GUTS!

Estúpido! Imbécil! Great greedy-guts! Look what you do: my beautiful parrot ees escapado! Ees perdido!

The only witness to Balthazar's death, the only one who could have talked, and there he goes.

The parrot ees give me by my grandfather. Ay, qué desastre . . . All same, muchas gracias for try to catch heem.

That's quite all right.

"Give to me by my grandfather". Why tell a lie? I wonder, could he be interested in the parrot for the same reason as me?

Meanwhile . . .

It's raining, Professor. Don't forget your umbrella . . . and remember your glasses.

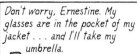
Don't worry, Ernestine. My glasses are in the pocket of my jacket . . . and I'll take my umbrella.

PWARK

PWARK PWARK ?

What a curious-looking creature!

I must take a closer look . . . Now, where have my glasses gone? I know I put them in my overcoat pocket . . .

Oh, it's a bird.

Good morning. How d'you do? Pleased to meet you!

I . . . er . . . do forgive me, sir. I'm so absent-minded . . . Would you believe it: I mistook you for a bird!

Your advertisement reads "Lost: magnificent parrot. Large reward. Finder contact 26 Labrador Road." It will be in tonight's paper, sir.

Ees necesario to make advertisement about the parrot.

There: "Lost: magnificent parrot . . ." Look, there are two notices, I'll try the first address: it's nearer than the other.

The sooner the better!

Grrreat greedy-guts!

RRRRING

I came about the parrot. Are you the gentleman who . . . ?

Ah, yes! Do come in!

Let's have a look . . .

It's him all right! I can't thank you enough. You wouldn't believe what he means to me. Please take the reward.

Goodbye, and thank you.

It's me who's grateful!

Now, I want to hear Polly run through his part: "What the parrot saw." But first . . .

. . . I need to buy a cage. Look after that box, Snowy. I'll be back in a few minutes . . .

?

PWARK! PWARK!

GRRREAT GREEDY-GUTS!

?

Who does he think he is?!

Help! They're fighting! . . . I must be in time to save Polly!

WOOAH . . . GRR PWARK

Grrreat greedy-guts!

Here, have you noticed? . . . There are two advertisements: and no one has brought back the parrot. It makes me wonder . . . is someone on the track of Balthazar's killer? . . . Anyway, it's an address to remember: 26 Labrador Road.

Si, si . . . only two people see parrot escape . . . thees old greedy-guts and thees young man . . .

Where's that wretched parrot now?

CREAK

CREAK

No doubt about it . . . there's a burglar in the flat . . .

Careful . . . he's in there . . .

Put your hands up!

I AM BALTHAZAR!

And I'm Colonel Barker! Surrender! You are surrounded!

Grrreat greedy-guts! . . . I am Balthazar!

Faithful unto death: a loving pet! Last night the occupants of 21 London Road, awakened by strange noises, found . . .

This time my luck's in! Quick! A taxi! . . .

TAXI! . . .

TAXI!

I give up. We'll have to walk.

Oh? The parrot? You really are unlucky. The gentleman who bought it yesterday came to collect it again . . . Not ten minutes ago . . .

He beat me to it, the gangster. And now he's got the parrot back.

LOOK OUT!

Look, Snowy! You see: 169 MW. Now watch: one . . . two . . .

Three! . . . Presto! . . . MW 691!

They just turned their numberplates upside down . . . Perfectly simple!

Now then . . . MW 691 . . . Alonso Perez, engineer, Sunny Bank, Freshfield . . . Not far from here to Freshfield . . . Let's go!

That night . . .

WHACK

Caramba! . . . Again ees too much to right!

Ha! ha! ha! . . . Caramba! . . . WHOOPEE!

Estúpido parrot! You shut up!

All you need do is aim more to the left: that way you hit the bull's-eye . . .

Muy bien, aim more to the left? . . . Why not?

GRRREAT GREEDY-GUTS!

Silencio! Silencio! Animal maldito!

Grrreat greedy-guts! Grrreat greedy-guts! PWARK! PWARK!

You!! . . . You take that!

You fool! What are you doing? . . .

Carrramba! . . . Missed again! . . .

WHACK

Crazy idiot! Think what that parrot means to us! Are you out of your mind? What about the fetish?

Fetish! Fetish! Al infierno weeth thees fetish! . . . And I wreeng the neck of thees feelthy parrot! . . .

Calm down, Ramón!

Carrramba! . . . Ha! ha! ha! . . . Grrreat greedy-guts!

Caramba!

Now, clever Señor Tortilla, the fun begins!

Several days later . . .

Well? Still nothing?

Nothing. No sign of heem anywhere!

Perhaps he see us and he keep to hees cabin . . . Or maybe he nevaire come aboard thees ship . . . Een thees case . . .

Ssh! Someone's coming . . .

Did you see? . . .

That feegure . . . eet could be . . .

Tintin, couldn't it?

No, ciertamente ees impossible! . . . Also, how could he know?

Sssh!

Or him?

It's crazy! We've started seeing Tintins around every corner! They're all fairly short . . . OK . . . But what does that prove?

. . . Ees right.

But no, ees not right! Eet ees heem! Ees first one, thees one in the cap. I remember heem: ees in same aeroplane and he seet behind us. Ees following us. I tell you, ees Tintin!

All right, there's only one answer. He's got to go!

Esta noche . . . tonight, after the dinner, we feex heem good!

That evening . . .

Now don't forget: aim a little more to the left . . .

Goodnight! . . . Oh!

Goodnight to you!

A weeg! Ees wearing a weeg! Ciertamente ees heem!

Careful, he's coming! Now above all, don't miss!

OOH! . . . HELP! . . . MURDER! HELP!

STOP THEM!

HELP! HELP! MURDER!

Madre! Ees close theeng . . . And to think I meess heem as well! . . . Ees your fault. You weeth your "Leetle more to the left"!

Well, it's the first time you landed where you aimed . . . Anyway, it's probably a good thing you didn't hit him, since it wasn't Tintin!

Ees right. But I could swear eet ees heem . . . Only hees voice when he shout ees not heem.

There's still the other: the little old man.

Next morning . . .

You are ready? We now go to work weeth thees leettle old man . . .

Ees heem!! He spy on us!

OK, let's see. We'll follow him . . .

No, not that way. We aren't sure it's him. I've a better idea: come with me . . .

Get it? If it's Tintin, he must be wearing a false beard. So . . .

Steady! . . . You're nearly there . . . A little to the right . . . Gently . . . Back a bit . . . That's it! . . . Now!

No, it isn't Tintin!

Now we're sure Tintin isn't aboard we can really get down to finding Tortilla . . .

. . . weeth fetish!

Ah, there's our steward . . . Will you join us for a drink?

Thanks . . . I see you're up bright and early. Not like some I could mention . . . Take your fellow countryman in cabin 17 . . . Never shows his nose outside the door . . .

Why not? Sick?

He says he is, but I don't believe a word of it. Anyway, he hasn't left his cabin since we sailed . . . Has all his meals there . . . Well, cheers!

Cheers!

You heard that? The passenger in 17 . . .

And you'll never believe it . . . Just between the three of us . . . the passenger . . . isn't a man, isn't a woman . . . but . . . an omelette!

? ?

Ha! ha! ha! Now wait for it . . . D'you know why? . . . Because he's called Tortilla, and in Spanish tortilla means . . .

. . . an omelette! Ha! ha! ha! That's rich!

Ees beeg joke! . . .

Got to go now . . . If the Captain sees me here I'll catch it . . . And you wouldn't want to drop me in the drink, eh?

Get away with you . . . you're a real caution!

That was a good one . . . drop in the drink . . . Get it?

Thanks to that nitwit we've found Tortilla . . . Ramón, the fetish is ours!

At last!

That night . . .

SPLASH

Next morning the ship arrives off Los Dopicos, capital of the Republic of San Theodoros, South America

Have you heard? . . . That Tortilla . . . He's disappeared! He must have been pushed overboard! There'd been a struggle in his cabin!

How shocking! . . . Do they know who did it?

They do indeed, gentlemen! . . . Come on now! . . . Get your hands up . . . fast!

Caramba! It's Tintin! I might have known!

Keep a close watch on them till the police arrive . . .

I am Colonel Jimenez, regular army.

Captain Maldemer . . . I have two prisoners I'd like to hand over, Colonel.

These two? . . . I know them both . . . dangerous crooks, wanted by our police.

Good idea of yours to meet the boat . . . Excellent . . . But there's still the fetish . . .

Don't worry . . . they won't have it for long!

. . . And that's the whole story. Look, here's the fetish they stole from the wretched Tortilla. Does anything in particular strike you about it?

I reckon it's another fake. The right ear isn't broken.

Exactly. So we still need to know two things. First, where's the real fetish . . . and then, what are all these gangsters really after?

RAT TAT TAT

Come in!

A letter for Mr Tintin, sir. A police launch just brought it.

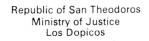

Republic of San Theodoros
Ministry of Justice
Los Dopicos

The Minister presents his compliments to Mr Tintin and requests his presence ashore to assist in the interrogation of two suspects. Mr Tintin is further invited to bring with him the stolen fetish. An officer will meet Mr Tintin on shore and put himself at his disposal.

Things are beginning to move. I'll just get myself ready and then I'll go.

See you later! Good luck!

Thanks. Goodbye.

Don't forget, we'll be sailing tonight at eight o'clock.

Don't worry, I'll be back. I don't want to get stuck in this place!

All right then, that's understood. You'll pick me up here at 19.00 hours.

Yes, sir.

Now we just have to wait for that obliging officer to come and put himself at my disposal!

Hey! My suitcase!

Well, well, here I am again . . . in the soup!

Still, it's not so bad. The launch from the "Ville de Lyon" is due to pick me up at seven. When I don't appear they'll go back to the ship and alert the Captain . . . He'll get me out easily enough.

Doesn't that dog belong to the lad they just took in?

Yes, and I guess he'll have a long wait for his master . . .

19.00 hours . . .

Perdone, señor teniente, but are you waiting for a young man to take out to the "Ville de Lyon"?

Yes, how d'you know that?

Because he said to tell you not to wait for him. And here's a letter he asked me to give you . . .

"To the Captain of the Ville de Lyon." All right, thank you.

That's that taken care of!

There's the launch going back. They'll warn the Captain.

. . . And there's the letter the man gave me.

Las Dopicos

Dear Captain,
As you know, I planned to continue my trip with you.
However, something new has come up concerning the theft of the fetish, forcing me to stay longer in Las Dopicos.
I am extremely sorry if I have incon-

What's happening? It must be nearly eight o'clock and the launch still isn't back . . .

TOOOOT TOOOT

That's the "Ville de Lyon"!

They're weighing anchor . . . sailing without me!!

This time it's hopeless . . . I can't see any way to get myself off the hook . . .

And next morning . . .

Squad! . . . Ready! . . .

Take aim . . .

Stop! Don't shoot!

Hello? What's up? Have I been reprieved?

Comrades! The revolution has triumphed! General Tapioca has fled, the tyrant is on the run! Our glorious General Alcazar is now in command!

Long live General Alcazar!

Down with Tapioca!

¡Fuera los tiranos!

¡Viva la libertad!

In which case, sir, you are free . . .

That suits me!

Colonel! . . . Ah, Colonel! At last I've found you!

Now what's going on?

What is it Colonel? Have they caught General Tapioca?

Caught him? . . . You couldn't be more wrong, Colonel! . . . General Alcazar's troops have surrendered. Alcazar himself has fled the country. General Tapioca is now in command!

Are you sure, Colonel?

Sure as eggs are eggs. I've been looking for you for half an hour to break the news!

Hmm . . . . In that case . . .

Comrades! The rebellion is crushed! General Alcazar has fled, the tyrant is on the run! Let us all swear allegiance to our glorious    General Tapioca!

Long live General Tapioca!

Down with Alcazar!

¡Fuera los tiranos!

¡Viva la libertad!

I'm terribly sorry, sir, but the way things are, I'll have to carry out my orders and shoot you.

!

Take aim . . .

FIRE!

This is it! I'm dead!

No I'm not! ... What ... what are they waiting for?

Caramba! My gun's been tampered with!

Sabotage!

Mine's the same, Colonel!

And mine too!

¡Mil bombas! Traitors in our ranks! ... Go and find some more rifles ... and at the double! ... Move yourselves!

You'll have to excuse us, sir: a technical hitch ... While we wait, would you care for an aperitif?

??? ... An aperitif? ... After all, why not?

¡Salud! ... By and large, being shot is just a nasty moment that's soon over, eh? One shouldn't take it too seriously.

Q ... q ... q ... quite right! ... Cheers!

Ugh! ... Wasn't that a bit strong?

You find it strong, eh? Aguardiente ... it's our local brandy ... Here, another little drop will do you a power of good ...

Half an hour later ...

My dear friend, I see my soldiers are back with more rifles. Shall we join them?

Only too glad ...

You're a good sort, Colonel ... Let's be friends ... lifelong friends ... till death us do part!

Till death us do part!

Squad! ... hic ... R ... r ... hic ... r-ready ... hic!

Long live ... er ... long live General Alhambra ... no ... General Alcazar ... Long live General Alcazar!

Bing! Bang! Boom! ... I'm dead! ... Long live General Alcazar and Uncle Tom Cobbleigh and all!

BANG

Oh dear, oh dear ... Rebels!

BANG

BANG

Run for it!

BANG

You're safe now!

That's OK by me! ... Then you can shoot me again ... Long live General Alcazar, bless his cotton socks!

He's one of the General's bravest supporters. They had their guns trained on him, and he was still shouting "Long live General Alcazar!"

¡Viva el héroe!

Yoohoo!

¡Viva el héroe!

Hooray!

Golly! . . . Look, there's Tintin!

Go and see what's happening, Colonel . . . and bring that young man here to me. I want to meet him.

I've already been shot three times . . . so a fourth time makes no odds to me. I'm used to it.

Here he is, General . . . he was sentenced to death by General Tapioca. Our men arrived just as the firing squad were going to shoot him. They had their rifles up, and this courageous fellow was still shouting "Long live General Alcazar!"

¡Muy bien! I am General Alcazar, and I need men like you! As a mark of my appreciation, I appoint you colonel aide-de-camp.

Thanks very much . . . but I'd like my hand back!

But . . . don't you think, General, it might be wiser to make him a corporal? We only have forty-nine corporals, whereas there are already three thousand four hundred and eighty-seven colonels. So . . .

Enough!!

I shall do as I like! I'm in command! But since you consider we are short of corporals I will add to their number. Colonel Diaz, I appoint you corporal!

Yes, General!

Here's your colonel's commission, young man. Now, go and get yourself kitted out. Corporal Diaz here will take you to the tailor.

Jolly old tailor!

A colonel's uniform for our young friend? . . . Excellent! I had this all ready for Colonel Fernandez, who fled with General Tapioca . . . He was just the same size . . . And for yourself? . . . A corporal's outfit? I have just the thing . . .

My career is in ruins. But I'll have my revenge, on you and that confounded General Alcazar!

*That night . . .*

Comrades, we have a new member . . . an officer who preferred to resign his commission rather than continue to serve a tyrant! He will take the oath.

I swear obedience to the laws of our society. I promise to fight against tyranny with all my strength. My watchword henceforward is the same as yours: liberty or death!

22

The next morning . . .

Where's my new aide-de-camp? Not here yet?

Not yet, General.

As soon as he arrives send him in. We have work to do . . .

Very good, sir. At once.

Colonel! . . . How on earth did I come to be a colonel? I don't remember a thing . . .

However, I'm still looking for the fetish, and to do that I must resign my commission.

No, gentlemen: impossible. The General is waiting for his ADC. He won't see anyone this morning.

Them!

Heem!

Oh!

Ah, there you are, Colonel. We must get down to work. As for you, gentlemen: I cannot receive you this morning . . . Come, Colonel!

No more need for me to resign, for the time being.

The General choose heem!

It's crazy!

Thees ees bad!

Yes, now we'll have to deal with him all over again!

Meanwhile . . .

His office window is open . . . So far so good!

It's a delicate position . . .

Yes, very delicate.

I'm sorry, Your Excellency, but the General can't see you this morning. The General is extremely busy . . .

Checkmate, my dear Colonel!

Goodness! You're right!

23

My dear Colonel, I shall never forget how you saved my life!

No, General, let's say I managed to save both our lives . . .

Caramba! Back to square one again!

We've been taken for a ride. The fetish he had in his suitcase was a fake. But he certainly knows where the real one is. So tonight, we'll have him picked up . . .

And we make heem tell us where the real fetish ees . . .

That evening . . .

What a wind! . . . We're in for a storm tonight . . .

Look! . . . He's coming!

HELP! HELP!

Whack! and off he goes to dreamland!

Get off!

An hour later . . .

That's agreed then: as soon as he's told us where the fetish is, we get rid of him for good!

Ees right: he gives us beeg trouble.

THUMP
THUMP
THUMP

Come!

We got him.

Good. Bring him in here . . .

Welcome to our humble abode, my dear Colonel! . . . Sit down and have a chat . . .

A neat trick, Colonel. The idea of putting a fake fetish in your suitcase wasn't bad . . . But now we'd like to know where the real one is . . .

Me too . . . I'd like to know that . . .

Come on! Cut the funny stuff! Where is it?

I've told you, I don't know.

Ah! Like that, is it? Very well.

I'll give you three minutes to answer my question. After that, a little squeeze with my finger and . . . click! . . . Understand?

BOMMM
BRROM
★

Caramba! Ees beeg storm! . . .

One minute . . .

If only . . . if only I could free myself . . .

Tintin? What's happened to Tintin?

Ees no use to struggle so hard, amigo. Ees good strong cord and tied very nice. You take my word for that . . .

Two minutes . . .

I must tell them something . . . doesn't matter what it is . . . otherwise I'm done for.

Thirty seconds to go . . .

All right. I'll tell you where to find the fetish . . .

Aha! . . . I knew we'd come to an understanding in the end. Where is it?

It . . . er . . . well, briefly, it's in my trunk aboard the "Ville de Lyon".

Thanks . . . That's all we wanted you to tell us.

And now we don't need you any more you can say your prayers! You're going to die!

Pronto, pronto, Alonso. You know I am upset by capital punishment . . .

Good old Snowy! There you are!

CÁRCEL

Good morning. I've brought you some customers!

Ten o'clock, and he still isn't here!

Now, quickly, back to the General.

RAT TAT TAT

Come in!

DYNAM

That's it . . . All I need is a light . . .

DYNA

DYN

DYNAM

¡Madre! I've forgotten my matches! . . .

DYNA

Hmm! . . . Surely I can smell something burning . . .

DYNA

Caramba! Back to square one again!

Check to your king, General!

Diablo! . . . I must watch what I'm doing . . .

That's checkmate, General!

¡Mil millón bombas! You dare to beat me, your General?!

BANG BANG BANG BANG BANG BANG

Ha! ha! ha! ha!

It's a little joke I often play on my officers, to frighten them. Naturally, my gun's always loaded with blanks.

That reminds me of an aide I had a while back. Ha! ha! ha! ha! . . . One day, he beat me at chess. I pulled out my gun . . .

This time, General Alcazar, your reign is at an end! Liberty or death!

DYNA

I pulled out my gun and fired. Ha! ha! ha! . . . Just imagine, the chap fainted . . . Ha! ha! ha! . . . And best of all, can you believe it, next day he had jaundice! . . . Imagine! Jaundice!

DYNA

BOOM

Justice is done!

AL
GENERAL
OLIVARD
LIBERTADOR
DE
SAN TEODORO
1805-1899

An attack!

The General's palace! . . . It's over there!

Another revolution? . . .

It's all right! Quite all right! General Alcazar is unharmed!

Idiot! Surely you know that if you just put dynamite against a wall it only produces a loud bang: you need to bury it . . . Now, it's back to square one again!

Next morning . . .

Hello? . . . Is that General Alcazar's palace? . . . Oh, it's you, doctor. How is the General? . . . What? . . . What?? . . . JAUNDICE!!!

Jaundice, yes . . . Caused by shock, you know . . .

RAT TAT TAT

Come!

Who is it?

R.W. Trickler, representative, General American Oil. All right, show him in.

Good morning. Do please sit down.

Well, Colonel, the reason I'm here . . . I heard yesterday . . .

Please excuse me . . .

Yes, of course . . .

Hello? . . . Hello? . . . Yes, Captain . . . What?! . . . They've escaped!

We are free, and soon the fetish ees ours!

And soon we'll have our revenge too; we have old scores to settle with Tintin!

Now, sir . . . I'm all yours . . .

Well, a geological survey party has just announced evidence of oil deposits in the Gran Chapo region . . . the desert lying partly in your own country and partly in the neighbouring territory, the Republic of Nuevo-Rico.

General American Oil seeks to obtain a concession to work these fields. Obviously, your government will have an interest in the profits that would accrue . . .

I see. I'm afraid General Alcazar is ill, and I cannot . . .

Of course, of course. But you could render us invaluable service. I mentioned that part of the oil fields lie in Nuevo-Rican territory. My company wishes to exploit the whole region: so it follows that you must take over the area.

But . . . that would mean war!

Unfortunately, yes. But what can one do? You can't make an omelette without breaking eggs, can you, Colonel?

So, here's the reason for my visit. We will give you 100,000 dollars in cash if you will persuade General Alcazar to undertake the campaign . . . Is it a deal?

?!!

You're making a big mistake in refusing my offer. But, just as you wish, Colonel! Goodbye!

A dangerous fellow! He could wreck all our plans. I must have a word with Rodriguez about him . . .

Ramón! What on earth . . . ? Are you hurt?

What happened? Quick, tell me . . .

Oooh! . . . He keell me! . . .

Here, sit down . . .

Ooooh!

YEOWW!

Who was it? Who paid you to get rid of me?

It was Rodriguez . . . Mr Trickler's right hand man . . .

I see . . . Now get up. I forgive you.

Oh, thank you, thank you, señor Colonel. I am your devoted servant . . . for life!

I really think he meant it, poor devil!

You shouldn't trust a rascal like that. You're far too gullible!

Some days later . . .

The General is back: he's completely recovered. At the moment he's talking to Mr Trickler.

Look, General . . . just think . . . It's wholly to your advantage. As I say, you declare war on Neuvo-Rico, and you annexe the oilfields. My company makes a profit on the oil and your country gets 35%. But naturally you deduct 10% for personal expenses . . .

Yes . . . very neat . . . I accept.

Excellent, General. I was sure we would understand one another.

By the way, General . . . that Colonel Tintin, in whom you seem to have so much confidence . . . Let me give you some advice: don't trust him. I won't say any more now . . .

Good morning, my dear Colonel . . . The General awaits you . . .

Good morning, General. I'm glad to see you're better. I . . .

What is it now?

!?! He doesn't seem in a very good mood today . . .

Send him in.

Basil Bazarov

KORRUPT ARMS GMBH

Good morning, General Alcazar. I happened to be passing through your country, and thought I'd show you our latest models.

This is our very newest line: the 75 TRGP. It's a really high-quality product: flexible, easy to handle, strong, and it will toss a nice little nickel-plated shell for you over a distance of 15 kilometres.

Oho! This could be serious. Listen, Ramón. Las Dopicos. A detachment of Nuevo-Rican soldiers crossed into the territory of San Theodoros and opened fire on a border post. Guards returned the fire and a violent battle ensued. The Nuevo-Ricans were forced to retire across the frontier, having sustained heavy losses. The only casualty on our side was a corporal, wounded by a cactus spine.

The airport . . .

Now we are off to San-Facion . . . the Nuevo-Rican capital.

Very good, sir.

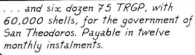

. . . and six dozen 75 TRGP, with 60,000 shells, for the government of San Theodoros. Payable in twelve monthly instalments.

To General Mogador's palace.

Very good, señor.

Half an hour later . . .

Back to the airport.

Si, señor.

That's Señor Bazarov's private plane . . .

. . . and six dozen 75 TRGP, with 60,000 shells, for the government of Nuevo-Rico. Payment in twelve monthly instalments.

Here he comes, back already to Las Dopicos.

Well?

All done. Another fat order . . . and something to fix Colonel Tintin too!

Now pay attention. It's a time bomb, with a clock. It's set to explode at exactly eleven o'clock tomorrow morning . . . And you'd better succeed this time!

I'll succeed, chief! Liberty or death!

The next morning . . .

General, I warned you against Colonel Tintin . . . Look at this letter and tell me if I was wrong . . .

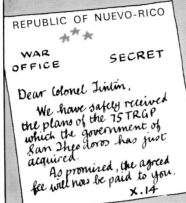

REPUBLIC OF NUEVO-RICO

WAR OFFICE    SECRET

Dear Colonel Tintin,
    We have safely received the plans of the 75 TRGP which the government of San Theodoros has just acquired.
    As promised, the agreed fee will now be paid to you.
                        X.14

A spy! . . . ¡Mil bombas! Planted as a spy! . . . The traitor! . . . The rat! . . . He'll pay dearly for this!

Hello! . . . Hello! . . . Colonel Juanitos? . . . Take ten men and go and arrest Colonel Tintin at once! . . . Eh? What? . . . That's an order, Colonel! . . . Move!

Meanwhile . . .

The explosion is set for 11 a.m. . . . What's the time? . . . Hello, my watch has stopped!

Now, let's put it right . . .

CALLE DEL SOL

RAT TAT TAT

Come in!

Good morning, Colonel Juanitos. Good to see you . . .

I'm terribly sorry, Colonel Tintin, but I've been ordered to arrest you!

Arrest me? . . . Me?? . . .

There's been a power cut this morning, so all the municipal clocks have stopped. Go and put them right.

Ten o'clock. There's still some time before I need to deposit my little box of fireworks!

Ah, General Alcazar, you're going to repent making me a corporal! Insult me at your peril! Corporal Diaz takes his revenge!

ALCADIA

Yes, you can take these: they're my orders. The first concerns Colonel Tintin: he will be shot at dawn tomorrow. The other is for Corporal Diaz, my former aide-de-camp. I've made him a colonel again. He can resume his duties at once.

Back in gaol again! Unless I'm much mistaken, my friend Trickler has cooked this one up to get rid of me.

Oh! . . . It won't be easy to escape . . .

Nightfall, and I still can't see any way out . . . There must be something . . .

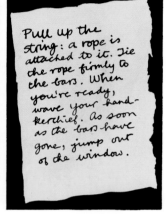

Pull up the string: a rope is attached to it. Tie the rope firmly to the bars. When you're ready, wave your handkerchief. As soon as the bars have gone, jump out of the window.

Ah, here comes the rope . . .

That's it: he's signalling! Pull!

Hello?

Come on, jump! Quick!

Tintin went past in a car . . . heading south!

I want him, dead or alive!

Next morning, at dawn . . .

There!!

It's him! . . . Open fire!

RAT TAT TAT TAT

Snakes! I'm being followed!

CRACK

X 14584

?

TOOOOOOT

Caramba! A train!! . . . We've got him. The road crosses the railway. He'll have to stop, or he'll be smashed to smithereens!

Tintin, my friend, this time it's all or nothing . . .

I'm staying here. Why climb down? He's had it anyway, hasn't he?

As you like. I'm going to see . . .

There it is. We can go back to Las Dopicos. That's put paid to Colonel Tintin.

VRROOM

What's going on up there?

?

That's our car!

!

He . . . he must have been hiding behind the rocks. I didn't see him coming . . .

It doesn't matter. He'll be caught at the frontier. It can't be far from here. We'll pick him up there. Come on!

?

It's a government car!

If they stop me, I'm caught . . . and if that's a strong barrier, I'm dead.

PAAAARP

CRACK

!

Hello? . . . Border post 31? . . . Patrol No. 4 here . . . A San-Theodorian car with a mounted machine-gun just raced past here, heading for the frontier.

Red alert! . . . San-Theodorian armoured car reported . . . Man your posts!

?

RATATATAT

Watch out, Snowy! . . . They're shooting at our tyres!

An armoured car tried to attack border post 31. It was destroyed and one of the occupants, a colonel, was taken prisoner.

*In Sanfacion . . .*

General! . . . General! . . . This dispatch has just come by telephone!

"An armoured car . . ." *!!! This time it's war! That's what they want: that's what they'll get!*

Pass this communiqué to the newspapers. I want special editions on the streets in an hour!

Sanfacion Star! . . . Extra! . . . Extra! . . . Sanfacion Star! . . . Extra!

*WAR! IT'S WAR!* A motorised column of the San-Theodorian army mounted a surprise attack today, but the enemy were repulsed by our valiant troops, who inflicted heavy casualties . . .

LAS DOPICOS HERE WE COME!

ALCAZAR OUT!

DEATH TO ALCAZAR

Hello? . . . Mr Trickler? . . . Success! The Nuevo-Ricans have just declared war on us! . . . Yes . . . over some new incident on the border . . .

The Gran Chapo fields are ours! . . . Once again General American Oil has beaten British South-American Petrol!

In a fortnight all the Gran Chapo will be in Nuevo-Rican hands. Then I hope you in British South-American Petrol will not forget your promises.

The first chance we get, we desert, and . . .

. . . we look for thees fetish again.

Meanwhile . . .

What will happen to me?

I don't know. We've been ordered to take you to Sanfacion, and that's all.

Good old Snowy! . . . Keep on chewing!

Free!

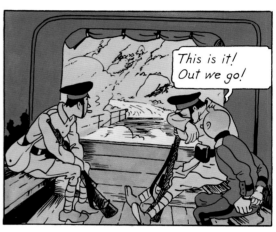

This is it! Out we go!

BANG BANG

BANG BANG

BANG

WOOAAAH!

SPLOSH

43

Hold your fire: he's out of range. Let him go. He'll be swept over the falls . . .

If I can't reach that rock. I'm done for!

Whew!

WOOAH!

Well, what do we do now?

?

A tree trunk! . . . Don't let it go . . . it could be our only chance!

Ah! It's swinging round!

That's it . . . We can get across . . . with luck!

We're safe now, Snowy.

The first thing is to find out where we are . . .

Meanwhile . . .

Caramba! Listen to this, Ramón . . .

Drama at sea. The liner "Ville de Lyon" caught fire last night in mid-ocean. Agency reports state that passengers and crew are safe, but all cargo and baggage have been destroyed.

The fetish! The fetish burnt!

Unless . . . unless thees Tintin is lying when he tell us thees fetish is in hees trunk . . .

A house, at long last!

He's lost, and is seeking shelter? . . . But of course, bring him in . . .

Don José Trujillo owns this hacienda . . . He is very happy to welcome you.

That evening . . .

So the river is the Coliflor? . . . Don't the Arumbayas live somewhere along the banks of the Coliflor?

Yes, they do. But there aren't many who'd dare go that way. The Arumbayas are the fiercest Indians in the whole of South America. The last man to try was a British explorer, Ridgewell. He went more than ten years ago. He's never been seen since.

Oh!

D'you think there's anyone who'd agree to take me there?

?

A dart! . . . It's sure to be poisoned! . . . D'you remember, Snowy? . . . Curare!

? ! ?

I can't hear anything now. I must have shaken them off . . .

?

Cowards! Come on out and show yourselves, unless you're afraid to!

Tintin, you'll get yourself killed!

WOOAH!

!

Great snakes!

A white man!

Who are you? And what brings you to this place?

My name is Tintin . . . who . . . who are you?

My name is Ridgewell.

Ridgewell? The explorer? But everybody thinks you're dead.

What a pity! Or rather, what a good thing, because I've decided never to return to civilisation. I'm happy here among the Arumbayas, whose life I share . . .

And whose weapons you've adopted. What was the meaning of that little game of darts?

I just wanted you to have an unfriendly reception, to encourage you to leave at once. Believe me, if I'd wanted to kill you it wouldn't have taken more than one dart. Look, I'll prove it. You see that big flower over there?

Yes.

Good shot!

?

WOOAAAAH!

Ooh! I'm so sorry!

WOOAAAH!

Don't worry, the dart wasn't poisoned. Use my handkerchief for a bandage.

Now, tell me how you come to be here in this country . . .

Well, it's like this. An Arumbaya fetish in a museum in Europe, brought back by the explorer Walker, was stolen and replaced by a copy. I noticed the substitution. Two other men were also on the track of the real fetish and whoever had stolen it.

I followed these two men to South America. They killed the thief on board ship and stole his fetish. But this one too was a fake. So now I'm trying to find the real fetish, and I still don't know where it is.

. . . Just as I still don't know what they were all after: Tortilla, the first thief, and his two killers. They all wanted the fetish. But why they wanted it is still a complete mystery. So I thought perhaps that here . . .

. . . among the Arumbayas I might learn something fresh about it . . .

Perhaps you may. It's quite possible . . .

Rumbabas! . . . Sworn enemies of the Arumbayas! . . .

What will they do to us? That's easy! They'll cut off our heads and by a most ingenious process they'll shrink them to the size of an apple!

Ahw wada lu'vali bahn chaco conats! Ha! ha! ha!

Just as I thought. He means our heads will soon be added to his collection!

They've gone . . . Snowy, you've absolutely got to save Tintin.

If I can find the Arumbaya village, and take this thing to them, perhaps they'll understand that its owner is in danger . . .

Meanwhile, in the Arumbaya village . . .

The Spirits tell me that if your son is to be cured, he must eat the heart of the first animal you meet in the forest . . .

I go, most powerful one!

What a strange animal! . . . And what's it carrying in its mouth? A quiver! That's funny . . . I must try to catch it alive . . .

See, O witch-doctor. This cloth belongs to the old bearded one, and the quiver also. Perhaps the old bearded one is in danger?

You mind your own business! . . . Give me the animal and go! . . . I shall kill the creature and take out its heart; this I shall give to your son to eat. Go now!

And if you breathe one word of all this, I shall call down the Spirits upon you and your family . . . and you will all be changed into frogs!

No danger now: he won't gossip . . . But he's right. The old bearded one may be in trouble. All the better! Let's hope he dies! Then I shall regain my power over the Arumbayas. Now, before I kill the animal I must burn these things . . . they might give me away.

Great Spirits of the forest, we bring thee a sacrifice of these two strangers . . .

Stop, O chief of the Rumbabas! The Spirits of the forest do not accept your sacrifice!

These two strangers are friends of the forest. You will set them free.

V-v-very w-w- . . . well!

It's magic . . . witchcraft!

Magic? . . . Didn't you realise it was me speaking? . . . I'm a ventriloquist . . . Ventriloquism, I'd have you know my young friend, is my pet hobby.

Good heavens!

Brother Arumbayas, you are about to witness a remarkable phenomenon . . .

My end!

We will take out this animal's heart and give it, still beating, to our sick brother . . .

YAAH!

The old bearded one!

The villain! . . . Lucky you decided to come and look for us Karamelo . . . otherwise we'd have been too late.

Let me introduce Avakuki, chief of the Arumbayas.

Owar ya? Ts goota meecha mai 'tee.

It's a pleasure, sir . . .

Naluk, Djarem membah dabrah nai dul? Tintin zluk infu rit'h. Kanyah elpim?

Dabrah nai dul? Oi, oi! Slaika toljah. Datrai b'giv dabrah nai dul ta'Walker. Ewuz anais-gi. Buttiz'h felaz tukahr presh usdjel. Enefda Arumbayas ket chimdai lavis gutsfa gahtah'z. Nomess in'h!

I was just asking the chief about the fetish, and this is what he told me . . . You'll be interested . . .

I'm all ears!

? ?

Nitwits!

Cohrluv ahduk! Ai tolja tahitta ferlip inbaul intada oh'l! Andatdohn meenis ferlip ineer oh'l!

I should never have started to teach them golf! They just can't learn to play properly!

!

But to come back to the fetish. The elders of the tribe still remember about the Walker expedition. It's quite a tale. They know that a fetish was offered as a token of friendship to Walker during his stay with the tribe. But as soon as the explorers had left . . .

the Arumbayas discovered that a sacred stone had disappeared. It seems that the stone gave protection from snake-bite to anyone who touched it. The tribe remembered a half-caste named Lopez, the explorers' interpreter, who was often seen prowling around the hut where the magic stone was kept under guard.

The Arumbayas were furious. They set off in pursuit of the expedition, caught up with them, and massacred almost all the party . . . Walker himself managed to escape, carrying the fetish. As for the half-caste, although badly wounded, he too got away. The stone, probably a diamond, was never recovered . . . That's how the story goes.

Now I understand . . . The whole thing makes sense!

Listen! . . . The half-caste steals the stone, and to avoid suspicion he conceals it in the fetish. He thinks he'll be able to get it back later on . . .

But the Arumbayas attack the expedition and Lopez is wounded. He has to flee without the diamond. And that's it! . . . The diamond is still in its hiding-place, and that's why Tortilla, and after him his two killers, tried to steal the fetish.

It looks to me as if you're right!

So now all I have to do is find the fetish . . . and return to Europe!

Some days later . . .

Meanwhile . . .

REPUBLIC OF SAN THEODOROS
NOTICE
DESERTERS
ALONSO PEREZ
RAMON BADA

We simply must get hold of a canoe . . .

Look! . . . There ees canoe . . . and weeth one man only . . . But . . . I theenk I am seeing theengs . . . or ees a dream . . . Thees man . . .

Caramba! . . . It's Tintin!

We'll rest here for a while before we continue our journey . . .

So we meet again, eh?

?

Let's start talking! . . . Did you know the "Ville de Lyon" had been completely destroyed by fire . . . burnt out!

Really?

Yes, really! And the fetish you left in your trunk has been destroyed! . . . Burnt! . . . All because of you . . . You are going to pay dearly, my friend!

No! I told you . . . The real fetish wasn't aboard . . .

Good! . . . Now they're safely taken care of, let's see what he's got in his wallet.

OHO!

Arumbaya. I am dying. Valker expedition the diamond in the fetish the broken ear. Lopez

Where did you get this note? . . . Tell me!

In the ship, on our way to Europe. Tortilla dropped it. But we didn't know what it meant. Tortilla was just a fellow passenger. We only realised the significance of the paper when we read about the fetish being stolen from the museum . . . Then we decided we'd try to get the fetish away from Tortilla.

Excellent! . . . Now, the only thing we don't know is how Tortilla got hold of this note. But since he's dead, I don't suppose we'll ever discover that! . . . So now, gentlemen, let's get moving!

And behave yourselves!

What are you planning to do with us?

No problem. I shall hand you over to justice. I think you well deserve it!

Hand us over to justice? . . . Ha! ha! ha!

!

Don't count your chickens before they're hatched, my fine friend . . .

Teep heem een! . . .

?

Got you!

Bravo!

There! . . .

Hee's feenished! Look, Alonso. Thees piranhas, thees man-eating feeshes . . . they come for heem already.

55

Caramba! I didn't hit him hard enough. Look! He's recovered . . . He's reached the bank . . .

Bah! Leave heem! We shall be in Sanfacion long before heem . . .

No point in trying to recapture them for the moment . . .

We've got a tough job, Snowy old boy. We've got to make the journey on foot.

Off we go!

Several days later . . .

Sanfacion at last! . . . Thank goodness! . . . I really thought we'd never make it! . . .

To Europe? . . . A boat left yesterday. Now I'm afraid you'll have to wait for a week.

A whole week! Oh well, we'll use the time to get rested and sort ourselves out . . .

Listen to this, Snowy! . . . "The geological survey party just returned from the Gran Chapo report that they found no trace of oil in the area."

A week later . . .

. . . the news . . . A ceasefire has been arranged between the forces of San Theodoros and Nuevo-Rico. It is believed that a peace treaty will be signed in the near future.

Home again! It's good to be back where we belong, isn't it Snowy? . . . All we need now is to unearth the fetish, and everything in the garden will be lovely!

Good heavens! ... It's fantastic!

Think of the thousands of miles I've travelled to find this thing!

£100 ... Cheap at the price! ... But come to think of it, I should have asked how he managed to get hold of the fetish ...

?!?

£17.50 THE PAIR

!?! ... There's no mistake ... They've both got a broken ear! ... I can't believe it ... It's absolutely incredible!

This time I really will find out where they came from!

Good morning. Would you be kind enough to tell me who brought you those two fetishes?

Ah, yes, the two little fetishes ... who brought them to me? ...

A bit of a struggle, but at last I've got the address ... Mr Balthazar, 32 Lamb's Lane ... That isn't very far. We'll go straight there.

J.BALTHAZAR

32

This is it.

OFFICES AND WORKSHOPS

Here we are ...

OFFICES AND WORKSHOPS

Are you Mr Balthazar . . . brother of the sculptor who . . . er? . . .

Yes, I am. What do you want?

I wondered if you could perhaps tell me how you found the fetish you used as a model . . .

Oh, that's easy enough. I was rummaging around my late brother's things. The fetish was at the bottom of a trunk . . . But why do you ask?

Er . . . it's a long story . . . But . . . you've still got the original?

It's a funny thing . . . someone else came to ask me exactly that question, only three days ago . . . No, I haven't got it. I sold it. But I can tell you the address of the man who bought it.

Mr Samuel Goldbarr . . . a rich American! Snowy, we're going to pull it off . . . We'll find the real fetish!

I'd like to speak to Mr Goldbarr.

Mr Goldbarr is not at home, sir.

But, sir, I cannot . . .

That's all right. I'll wait for him.

But sir, you'll have a long wait.

It doesn't matter. I've got plenty of time.

But sir, Mr Goldbarr has left for America . . .

Left for America!!! . . . Oh!!

. . . He's sailing today aboard the SS Washington. Perhaps, if you hurry . . .

. . . and of course he had to take the fetish with him! That's just my luck!

Ex . . . ex . . . excuse me . . . the . . . the . . . the SS WASH . . . WASHINGTON?

That's her out there. If you wanted to board her you're too late. She sailed an hour ago.

But if you really want to catch her, maybe you could hitch a ride from the air-base over there . . . It's not far . . .

NO EN
EXCEP

. . . catch the "Washington", eh? . . . Hmm . . . maybe . . . We happen to have a plane going out to her . . . to deliver some mail . . .

First service for lunch, please! . . . First service for lunch! . . .

F·MAB

F·MAB

There goes Goldbarr . . . He's off to lunch. Now's our chance!

Ramón! . . . Ramón! . . . Look! . . . I've got it!

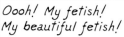

Oooh! My fetish! My beautiful fetish!

Mr Goldbarr? . . . I'm terribly sorry your fetish has been damaged. I can explain everything if you'll allow me . . .

. . . I think you should know that your fetish is stolen property.

Stolen?! . . . But I . . .

Yes, I know where you bought it, and I'm sure the man who sold it to you acted in good faith . . .

If that's the case, I wouldn't consider keeping the fetish for a moment longer. If you're going back on shore, can I ask you to take it and restore it to the museum where it belongs? I'd be greatly obliged!

OF ETHNOGR

May I please speak to the Director?

And now, Snowy my friend, we're going to take a well-earned rest!

Wooah! Wooah!

Toreador, on guard now! Torea- dor! Toreador!

ARUMBAYA FETISH
The Arumbaya tribe live along the banks of the River Coliflor in the Republic of San Theodoros, South America